FIRST TIME LEARNING

The Alphabet

3+

Preschool

The Alphabet

Key skills for early learning
Prepares for starting school

Here's a short note for parents:

We recommend that you work through this book with your child, offering guidance and encouragement along the way. Try to find a quiet place to sit, preferably at a table, and encourage your child to hold his or her pencil correctly. Try to work at your child's pace and avoid spending too long on any one page or activity. Most of all, emphasize the fun element of what you are doing and enjoy this special and exciting time!

Autumn Publishing

a b c d e f g h i j k l m

Pictures and letters

Find an apple sticker.
Here are some pictures.
Point to each one and say
the word.

Place your
sticker here

Here are the first five letters of the alphabet.

a b c d e

Now the letters have been jumbled.
Can you circle the first and second letters of the alphabet?

b c e a d

Place your
reward sticker
here

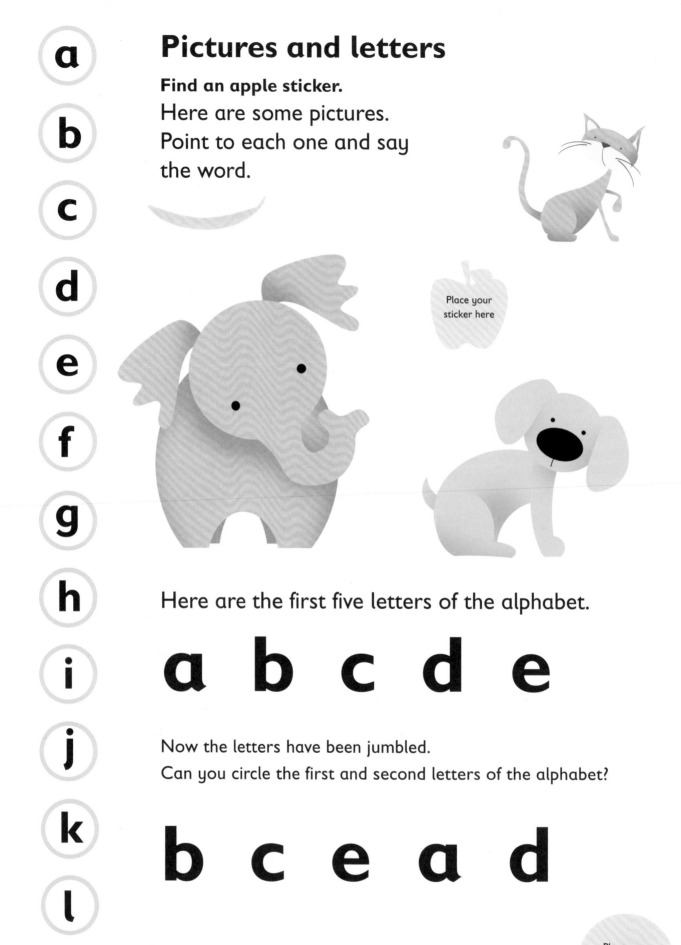

Find another picture

Find another picture exactly the same in each line and colour it.

Find another letter

Find another letter the same in each line and circle it.

a	c	e	a	b	d
b	a	e	d	b	a
c	d	c	d	a	e

n
o
p
q
r
s
t
u
v
w
x
y
z

Make the pictures the same

Find a cat sticker.
Look at the pictures.
Can you make the animals in each row the same?

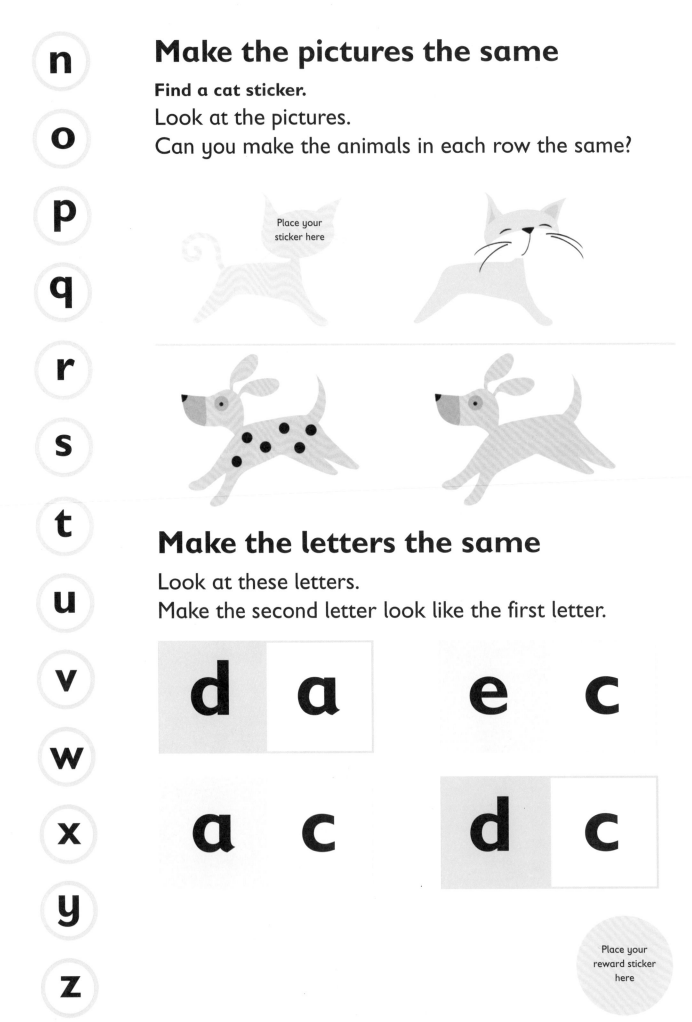

Make the letters the same

Look at these letters.
Make the second letter look like the first letter.

Once upon a time...

Do you know the story of 'Goldilocks and the Three Bears'?
Can you tell the story from these pictures?

a b c d e f g h i j k l m

Odd one out

Find the odd one out in each line and circle it.

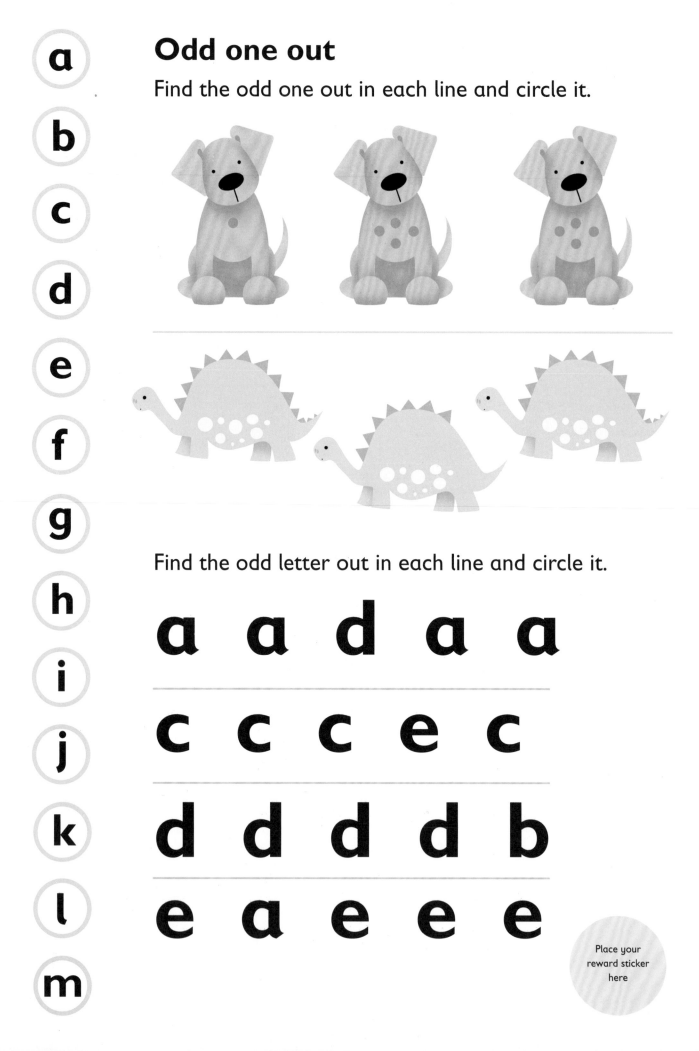

Find the odd letter out in each line and circle it.

a a d a a

c c c e c

d d d d b

e a e e e

Place your
reward sticker
here

Tell a story

Look at these four pictures.
Can you make up a story to go with the pictures?

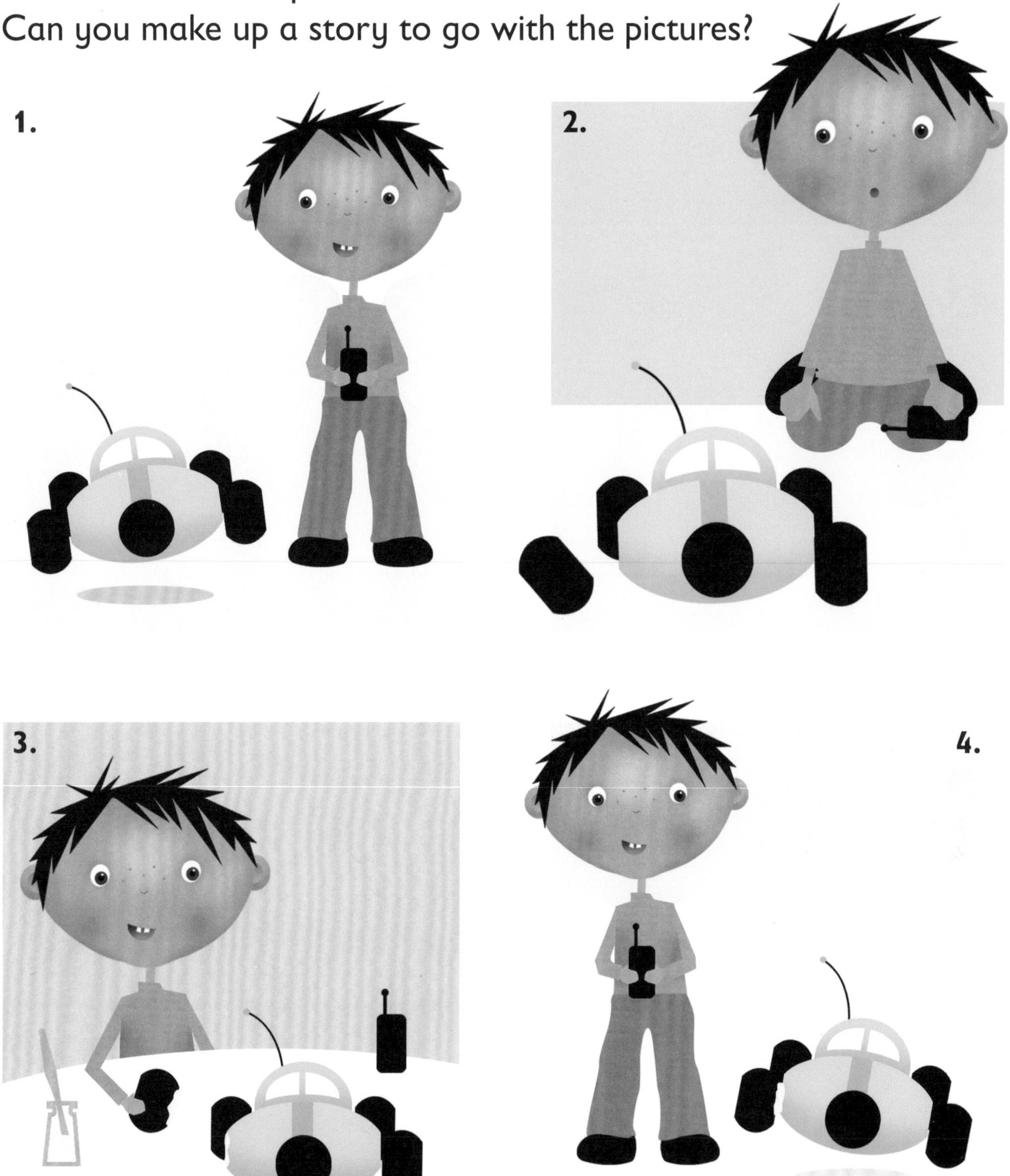

1.

2.

3.

4.

n
o
p
q
r
s
t
u
v
w
x
y
z

Let's start at the very beginning...

All letters have different sounds.

These things start with the letter **a**.

apple   **ant**

Say the letter sound at the beginning of each word.

Busy bee

Say the letter sound at the beginning of each word.

ball   **bed**   **bag**

Can you think of other words that begin with the **b** sound?

Note to parent:
The letter sounds are **'a'**, **'buh'** and **'kuh'**;
The letter names are **'ay'**, **'bee'** and **'see'**.

Place your
reward sticker
here

I spy

I spy with my little eye, things beginning with **c**.
Point to the pictures and say the words.

car   **cat**   **comb**

At the beginning

Find the missing letter sticker.
Draw a line to join each picture to the first letter of its name.

a   Place your sticker here   **c**

Place your reward sticker here

a
b
c
d
e
f
g
h
i
j
k
l
m

d e f

Look at the pictures.
Say the letter sound that each thing begins with.

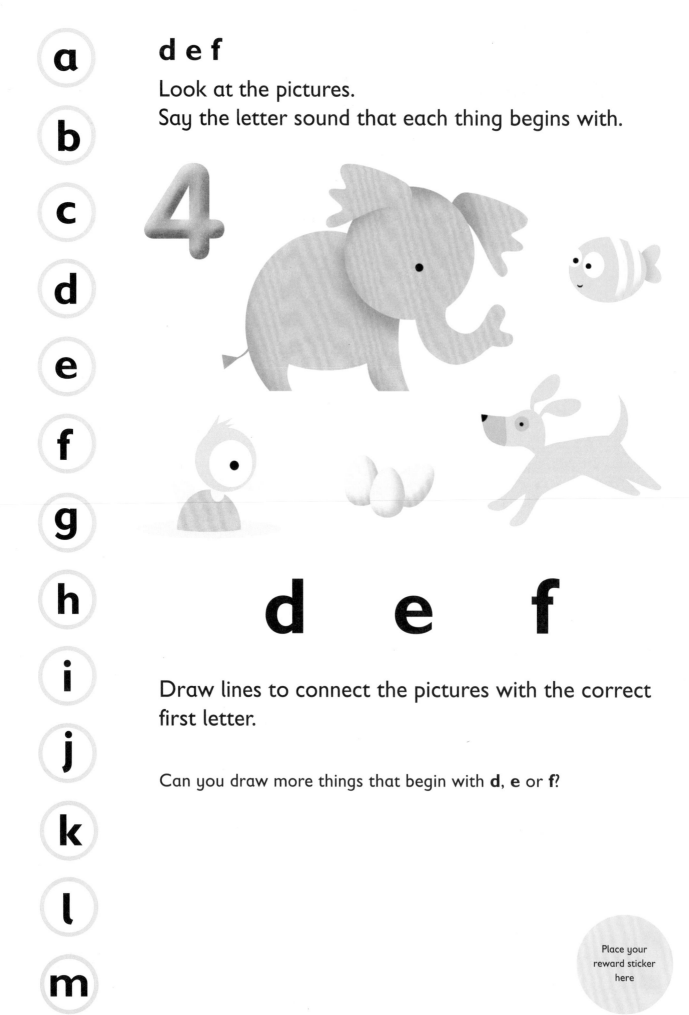

4

d   e   f

Draw lines to connect the pictures with the correct first letter.

Can you draw more things that begin with **d**, **e** or **f**?

Place your reward sticker here

I spy

I spy with my little eye,
something beginning with... **d**

Find a picture sticker of something beginning with d.

Colour f

Colour the things that begin with **f**.

n
o
p
q
r
s
t
u
v
w
x
y
z

g h i

Look at the pictures.
Say the letter sound that each thing begins with.

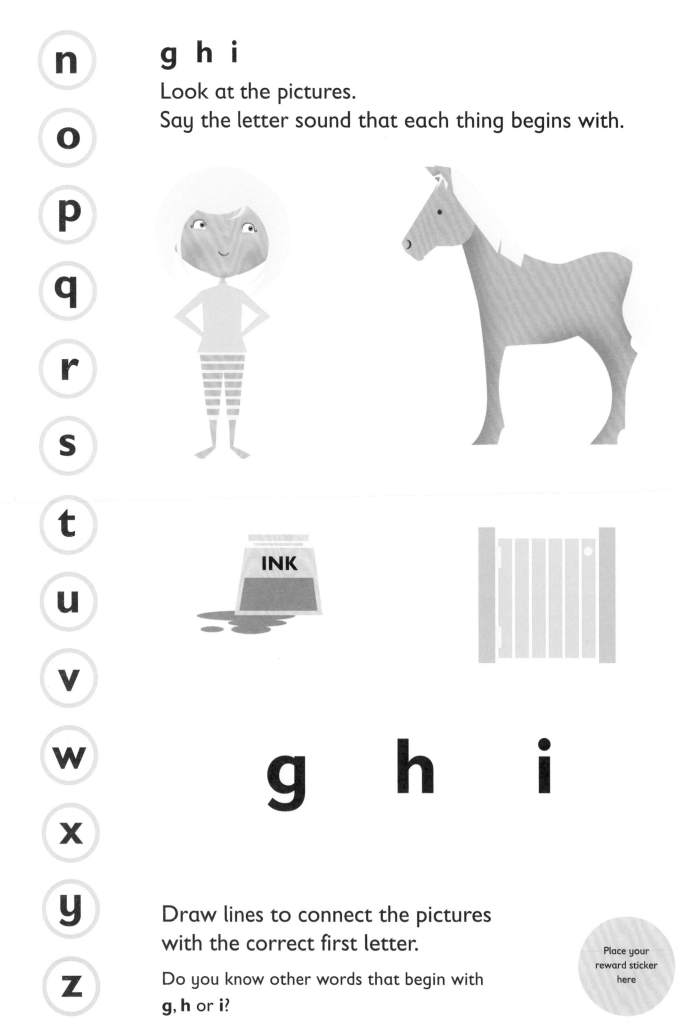

INK

g   h   i

Draw lines to connect the pictures
with the correct first letter.

Do you know other words that begin with
g, **h** or **i**?

I spy

I spy with my little eye, something beginning with… **g**

Place your sticker here

Find a picture sticker of something beginning with g.

Colour h

Colour the things that begin with **h.**

Place your reward sticker here

a b c d e f g h i j k l m

j k l

Look at the pictures.
Say the sound that each thing begins with.

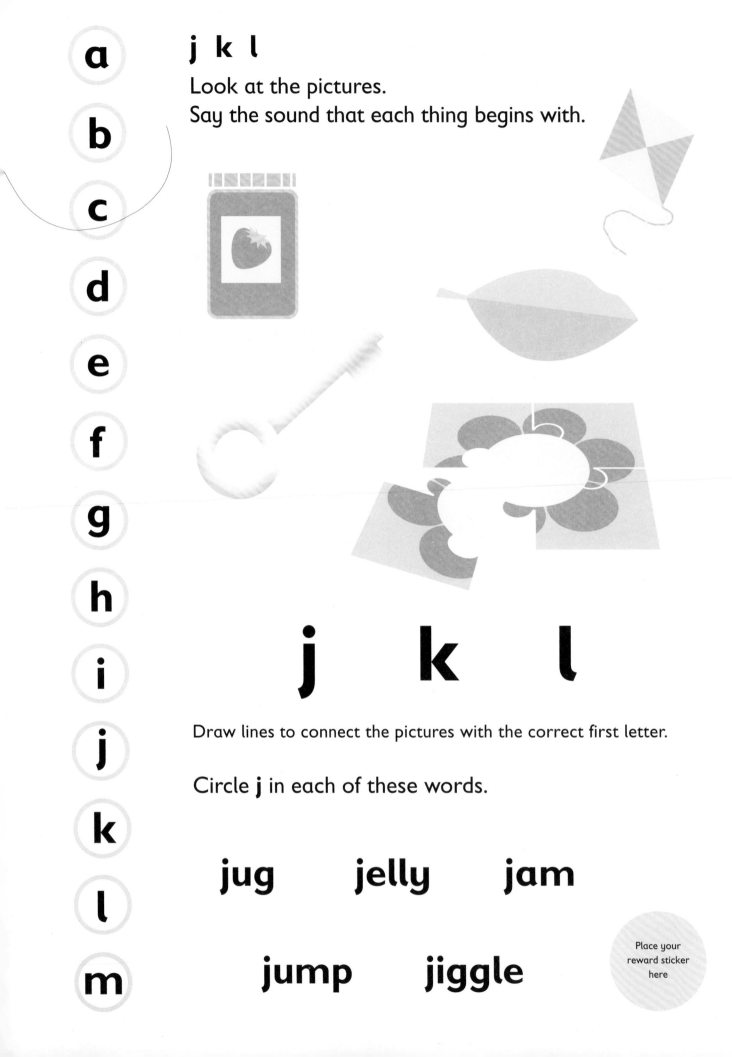

j   k   l

Draw lines to connect the pictures with the correct first letter.

Circle **j** in each of these words.

jug   **jelly**   **jam**

jump   **jiggle**

Place your
reward sticker
here

I spy

I spy with my little eye,
something beginning with… **k**

Find a picture sticker of something beginning with k.

Do you know other words that begin with **k**?

Little Lisa likes...

What does little Lisa like? She only likes things that begin
with the letter **l**.

Colour the things that Lisa likes.

n
o
p
q
r
s
t
u
v
w
x
y
z

Seeing double

Draw lines to connect the letters that are the same.

f g h i j k

i k f g h j

Look at the pictures and say the words.

Trace the first letter in each word.

house   helicopter

Find the letter 'h' sticker.

Place your sticker here

Place your reward sticker here

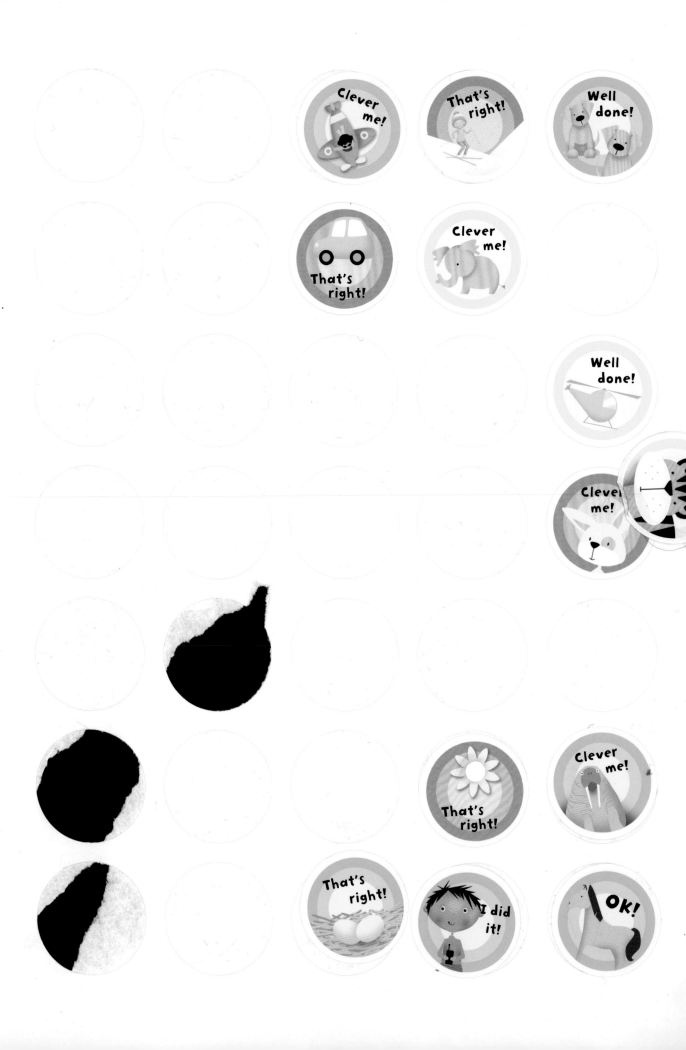

Sort the shopping

Draw lines to put the shopping in the correct trolley.

Find a sticker of something that begins with b.

Put it in the trolley.

Place your sticker here

Place your reward sticker here

a
b
c
d
e
f
g
h
i
j
k
l
m

m n o

Look at the pictures.
Say the letter sound that each thing begins with.

m n o

Draw lines to connect the pictures with the correct first letter.

Find the letter 'n' sticker.

Place your sticker here

Place your reward sticker here

I spy

I spy with my little eye,
something beginning with… **m**

Place
your
sticker
here

Find a picture sticker of something beginning with m.

Colour sounds

Colour the picture in each line that begins with the letter.

Place your
reward sticker
here

n
o
p
q
r
s
t
u
v
w
x
y
z

p q r

Look at the pictures.
Say the letter sound that each thing begins with.

p q r

Draw lines to connect the pictures with the correct first letter.

I spy

I spy with my little eye, something beginning with… **p**

Place your sticker here

Find a picture sticker of something beginning with p.

Do you know other words that begin with **p**?

Colour r

Colour the things that begin with **r**.

Place your reward sticker here

a
b
c
d
e
f
g
h
i
j
k
l
m

s t u

Look at the pictures.
Say the letter sound that each thing begins with.

s   t   u

Draw lines to connect the pictures with the correct first letter.

Circle **s** in each of these words.

sun   sand   star

snake   bus

Place your
reward sticker
here

I spy

I spy with my little eye,
something beginning with... **S**

Find a picture sticker of something beginning with s.

Do you know a long, slithery animal that begins with **s**?

Draw it here.

Colour t

Colour the things that begin with **t**.

n
o
p
q
r
s
t
u
v
w
x
y
z

v w x

Look at the pictures.
Say the letter sound that each thing begins with.

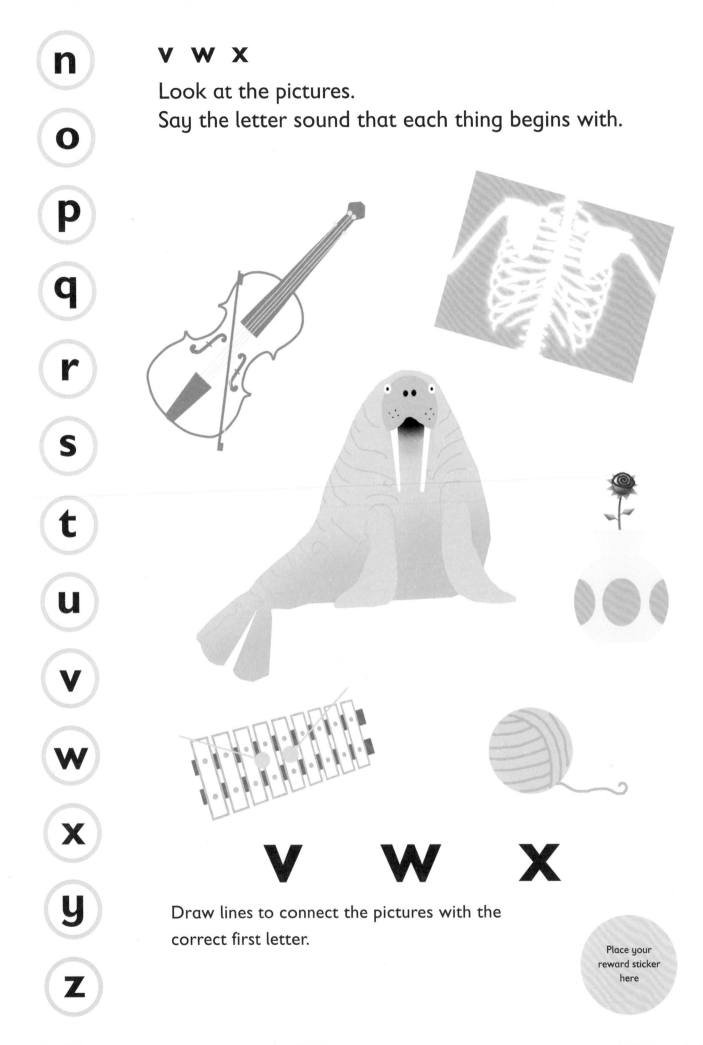

V   W   X

Draw lines to connect the pictures with the
correct first letter.

Place your
reward sticker
here

I spy

I spy with my little eye,
something beginning with… **W**

Place your
sticker here

Find a picture sticker of something beginning with w.

Do you know other words that begin with **w**?

Colour w

Colour the things that begin with **w**.

Place your
reward sticker
here

a
b
c
d
e
f
g
h
i
j
k
l
m

y z

Look at the pictures.
Say the letter sound that each thing begins with.

y z

Draw lines to connect the pictures with the correct first letter.

a is the first letter in the alphabet.
What is the last?

Place your
reward sticker
here

I spy

I spy with my little eye,
something beginning with... **Z**

Place your
sticker here

Find a picture sticker of something beginning with z.

Do you know other words that begin with **z**?

y is for yellow

Colour all these things yellow.

Place your
reward sticker
here

n
o
p
q
r
s
t
u
v
w
x
y
z

You name it

Can you think of a name for each of these animals?

Each name must start with the same letter as the animal.

A good name for the parrot would be Peter Parrot.

kangaroo

horse

zebra

monkey

Place your sticker here

panda

Find a sticker of
Peter Parrot.

Place your
reward sticker
here

I like...

Ben and Carl like things that start with the first letter of their name.

Draw a line to join Ben and Carl to the thing they like.

Ben

Carl

What's your name?

Draw pictures of things that start with the same letter as your name.

Here's Jenny.
**Find a sticker
of something
she likes.**

Jenny

Place your
sticker here

Place your
reward sticker
here

p is for party

Pete is having a party!
Colour the food that begins with **p**.

Find a sticker present for Pete.

His present begins with **p**.

What is it?

Place your
sticker here

Place your
reward sticker
here

It's in your name

Circle the letters that are in your name.

a b c

d e f g h

i j k l m

n o p q r

s t u v w

x y z

Place your reward sticker here

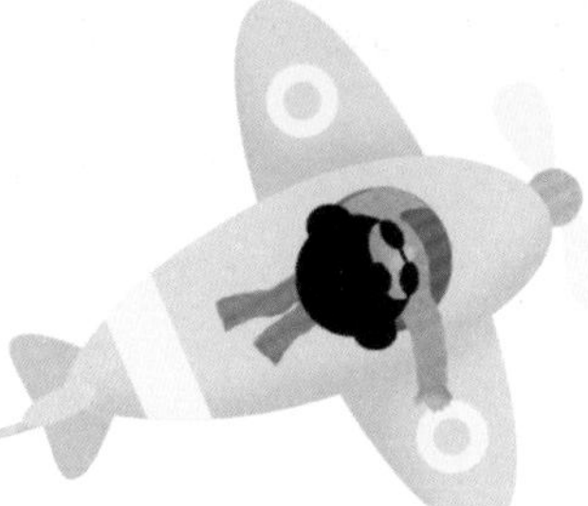

From a to z

Now you know all the letters from **a** to **z**!
Start at **a**, and join the letters in alphabetical order.
What have you drawn?

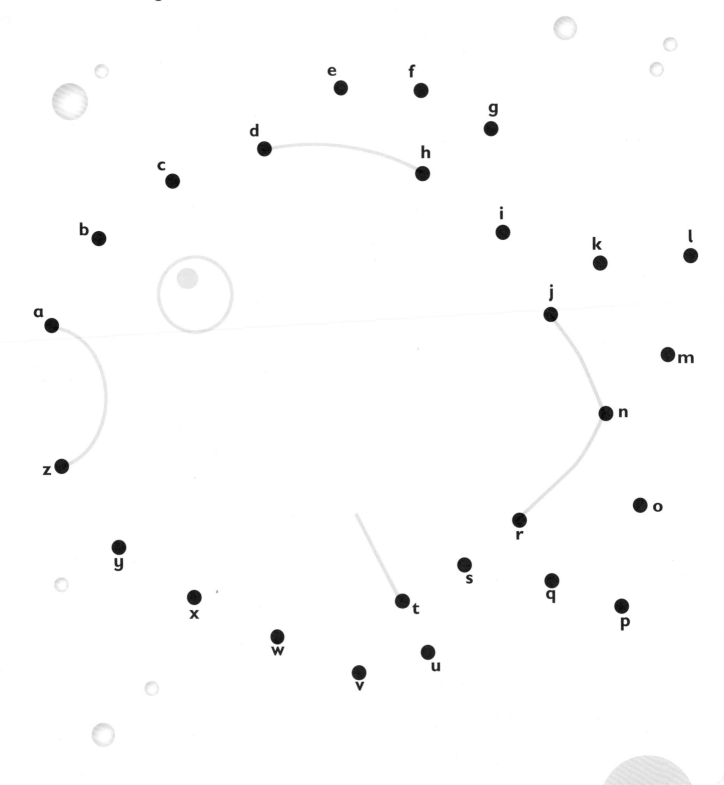

Well done! You're a star for finishing this book.

Place your reward sticker here